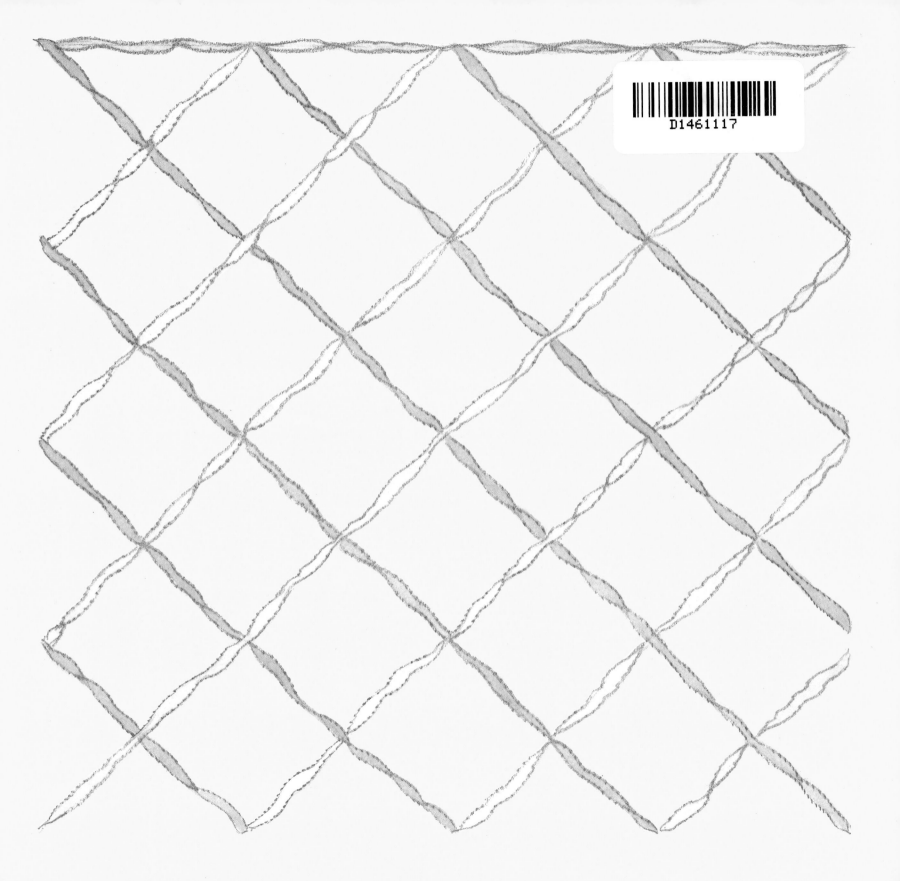

# Baby's First Years

## Illustrated By
## Ian Beck

### Text By
### Deborah Manley

conran
OCTOPUS

First published 1985
in Great Britain by
Conran Octopus Limited,
37 Shelton Street, London, WC2H 9HN
a part of Octopus Publishing Group

Designed by Heather Garioch

ISBN 1 85029 044 X

Printed in China

# Contents

# My Birth

I was _____ days old when this picture was taken

My hair was _____ My eyes were _____

I weighed _____ I was _____ long

I was born at

_____

on _____ 19_____ at _____ o'clock
My star sign is

_____

On the day I was born
my horoscope said

_____

_____

_____

# My Family

Here is my family tree

Grandfather and
Grandmother

————————————

————————————

Grandfather and
Grandmother

————————————

————————————

Father

————————————

Mother

————————————

My family name is

————————————

6

Here are photographs of some members of my family

# My Welcome

People who came to visit me were

_____

_____

_____

These are some of the gifts and flowers that people gave me and my mother

_____

_____

_____

This is how my birth was announced

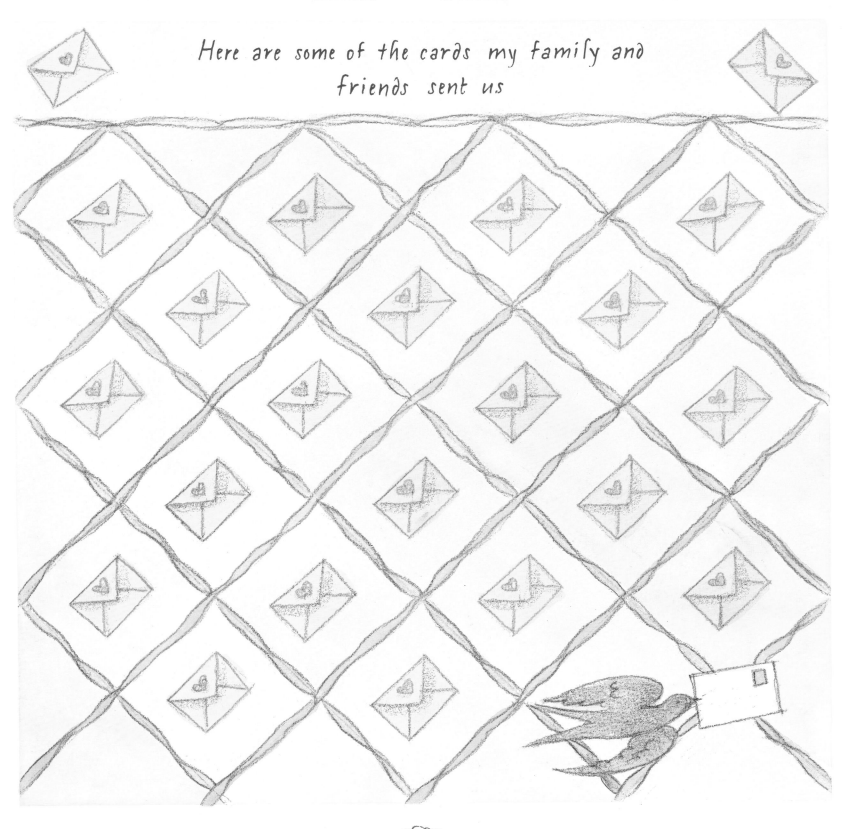

Here are some of the cards my family and friends sent us

# Going Home

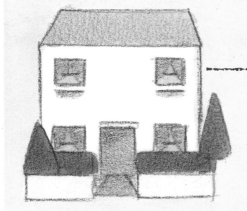

My first home was

_____

I arrived there on

_____

_____

brought me home

_____

was there to welcome me
I lived there with

_____

This is a picture of my first home

Here is a picture of the place where I live

# The World When I Was Born

## This is what was happening in my neighbourhood

Stick cuttings here
from your local newspaper about people,
events, new buildings, street scenes, etc. at the time
of your baby's birth.

# This is what was going on at the time

Stick cuttings here
about any main news events
during your baby's first week or two.

# My Christening

My full name is

_____

My parents chose my name · because

_____

My Christening was at

_____

on _____ 19____

The people who came to my christening were

_____

_____

They celebrated the occasion at

_____

This is a picture of me at my christening

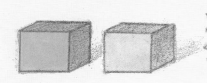
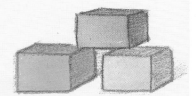

# As I Grow Up

This is how big my hand was

when I was ————————          and when I was ————————

This is how big my foot was

when I was ————————          and when I was ————————

You can record how fast your baby grows
by taking hand and foot prints in the first days and
adding outlines of the hand and foot at about a year old.
To make prints, press the baby's hand against a dye pad and
then onto a piece of paper, using a slightly rolling movement. Do the
same for the foot. Then cut out the prints and stick them into the book.
(Make sure that the ink of the dye is perfectly safe.) When your baby
is about a year old, add the outline of the hand and foot.
Draw around your baby's hand and foot with a pencil
onto a piece of paper. Cut out the outline and
stick it into the book.

age

height

age

weight

# My First Six Months

I began to watch my mother when I was _____

I first smiled at _____

I was sleeping through the night by _____

I discovered my hands at _____

I could hold a toy in my hand at _____

I first laughed at _____

I reached out and took a toy at _____

I discovered my feet at _____

I could roll over by _____

I knew my name when I was _____ months old

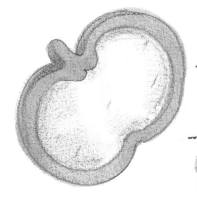

My favourite toy was
_____

My favourite game was
_____

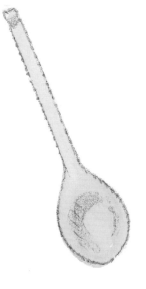

This is a picture of me
when I was_____
months old

# My First Teeth

Here is a picture of me with my first tooth

This is when my first teeth came through

1st tooth _____

2nd tooth _____

3rd tooth _____

4th tooth _____

5th tooth _____

6th tooth _____

I had all my teeth by

_____

# What I Liked To Eat

I had my first taste of solids when I was

_____

I was eating well from a spoon by

_____

I was eating finger foods by

_____

I was fully weaned by

_____

I could drink from a cup by

_____

I could feed myself by

_____

My favourite foods were

_____

But I did not like

_____

# My First Christmas

I spent my first Christmas at

_____

with

_____

I was _____ old

My presents were

_____

_____

_____

The weather on Christmas Day was

_____

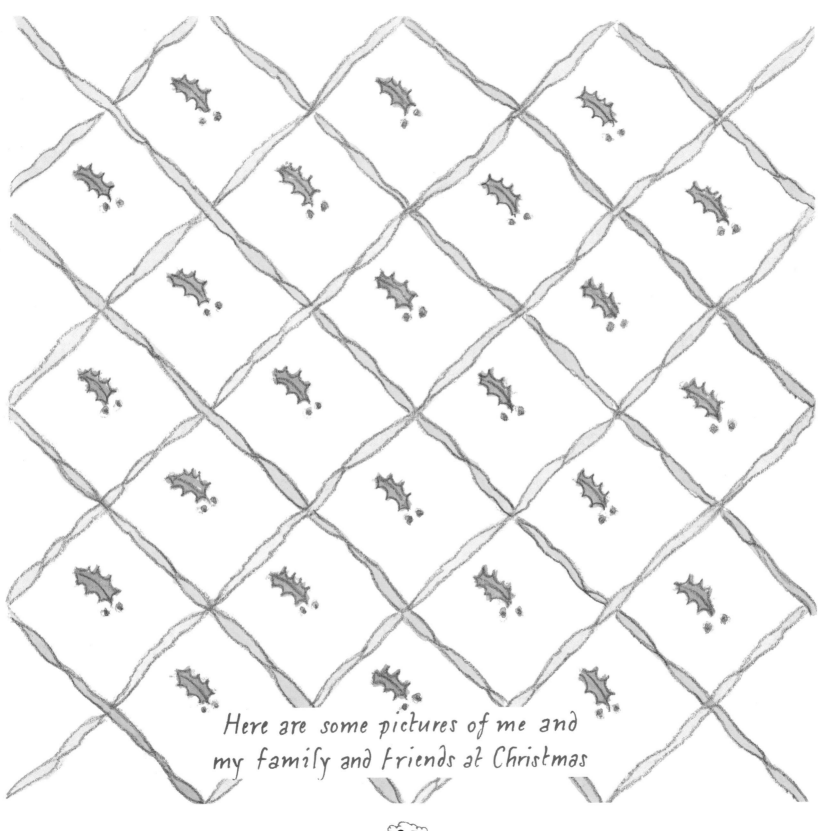

Here are some pictures of me and
my family and friends at Christmas

# My Second Six Months

I could sit up without support
when I was _____
I learned to point at things by _____
I first waved 'Goodbye' at _____
I copied sounds my parents made by _____
I could drop things onto the floor
on purpose by _____
By my first birthday I understood
these words _____

_____

_____

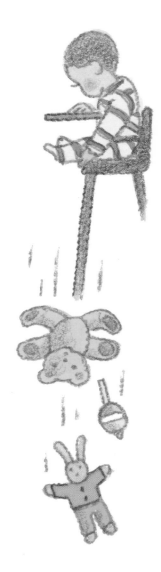

My favourite toy was ————————
My favourite game was ————————
My favourite song was ————————

Here are some pictures of me
when I was

————————————————

# When I Got Moving

I began to move myself along
when I was _____
I did this by _____
I could pull myself up
to stand by _____
I could stand alone by _____
I began to walk if I held on to
the furniture at _____
I took my first steps
on my own on _____
I had my first shoes on _____
They were _____
    colour
and they were _____
    size

Here are
pictures of me
when I was getting moving

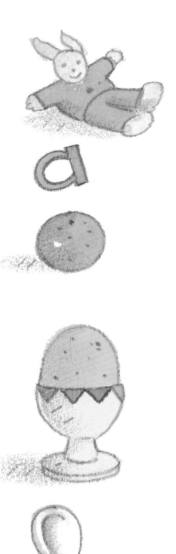

# What I Had To Say

**a** • **b** • **c**

The first words I understood were

_____

My first words were

_____

I could say these words when I was

_____

My own words for things were

_____ for _____

_____ for _____

_____ for _____

_____ for _____

My names for family and friends were

_____ for _____

_____ for _____

_____ for _____

_____ for _____

I called my toys these names

I called my \_\_\_\_\_ \_\_\_\_\_

I called my \_\_\_\_\_ \_\_\_\_\_

I called my \_\_\_\_\_ \_\_\_\_\_

I called my \_\_\_\_\_ \_\_\_\_\_

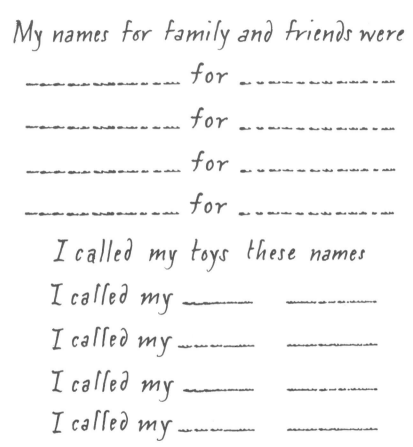

# My First Birthday

This is me on my first birthday

Mummy and Daddy gave me a

_____

My other best presents were

_____

I had _____ cards

I invited these people to my party

_____

_____

_____

# More About Me

When I was about a year old
I could do lots of things

My best trick was to

_____

I first helped my mother by

_____

I first helped my father by

_____

My favourite occupations were

_____

My favourite place to go was

_____

My favourite clothes were

_____

but I didn't like

_____

My favourite animals were

_____

My favourite music was

_____

My first friends were

_____

# My First Holiday

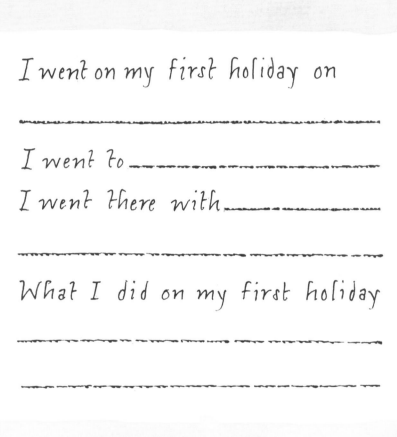

I went on my first holiday on

_____

I went to _____

I went there with _____

_____

What I did on my first holiday

_____

_____

Here are pictures of my first holiday

# My Second Christmas

I spent my second Christmas at

_____

with _____

I was _____ old

My presents were

_____

_____

_____

For Christmas dinner I had

_____

Here are some pictures of me and my family

# Milestones In My Second Year

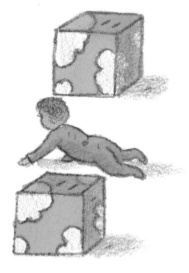

I started to go upstairs when I was

_____

I could put three bricks on top
of each other by

_____

I began to fetch things my family
asked for by

_____

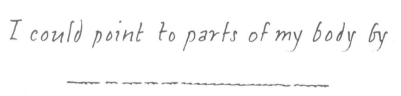

I could point to parts of my body by

_____

I had learned to run by

_____

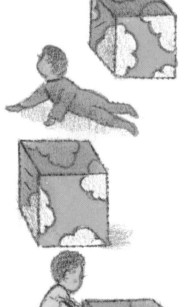

I could kick a ball by

_____

Here are some pictures of me during my second year

# My Second Birthday

This is me on my second birthday
Mummy and Daddy gave me

_____

My other best presents were

_____

_____

I invited these people to my party

_____

_____

This was my favourite card

# Milestones In My Third Year

I could build a tower
with _____ blocks by _____
By _____ I could dress myself
- though it wasn't always quite right !
I could jump with both feet by _____
I could walk on tip toe by _____
My favourite toys were

_____

My favourite games were

_____

My favourite stories were

_____

This is a picture of me when I was _____

My favourite songs were

_____

_____

The most exciting things that happened to me
in my third year were _____

_____

# My Third Christmas

Here I am at my third Christmas

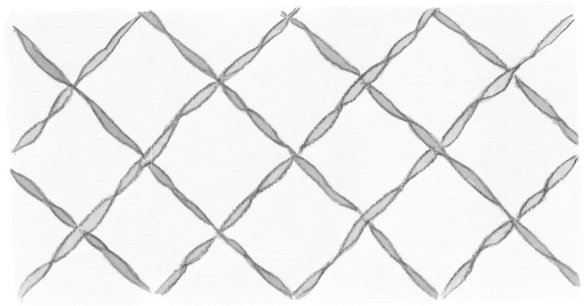

I spent it with

_____

My presents were

_____

# My Third Birthday

Here I am on my third birthday

These friends came to my party

# As I Grow Up

I started playgroup at

_____

on _____

I started school at

_____

on _____

My first teacher was called

_____

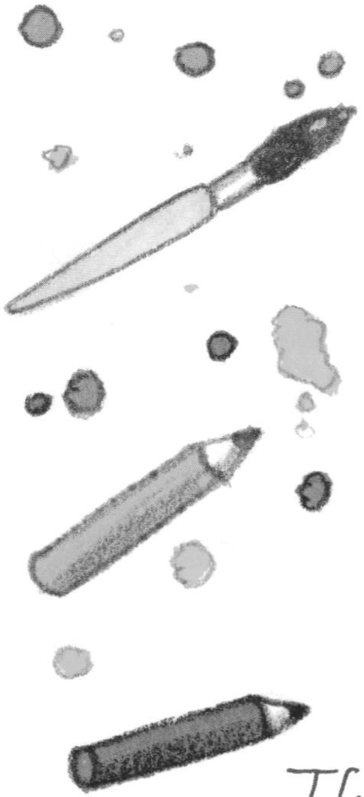

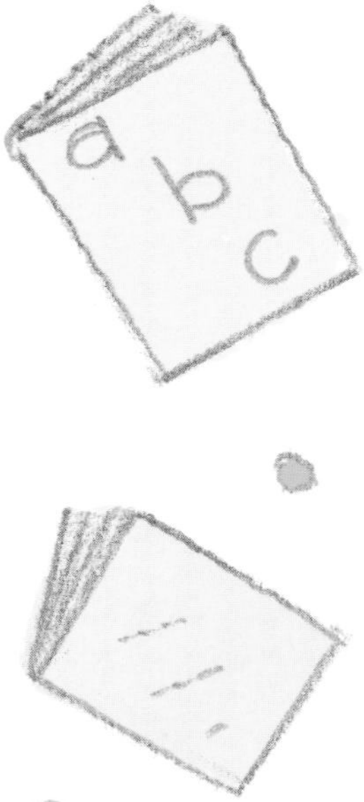

3+1=

This is me when I was four. I was _____ tall

This is me when I was five. I was _____ tall

This is me when I was six. I was _____ tall

# My Medical Information

My National Health Service number is_____ My blood group is_____

Telephone numbers:

Doctor_____ Health Visitor_____

Hospital _____

## MY IMMUNIZATION RECORD

Triple vaccination and poliomyelitis

1 (at about 3 months) on_____ 2 (at about 5 months) on_____

3 (at about 11 months) on_____

Measles

(at about 13 months) on_____

Pre-school booster

(at about 4½ years) on_____

## MY FIRST ILLNESSES

I had_____when I was_____old

I had_____when I was_____old

I had_____when I was_____old

I had_____when I was_____old

I had_____when I was_____old

I had_____when I was_____old

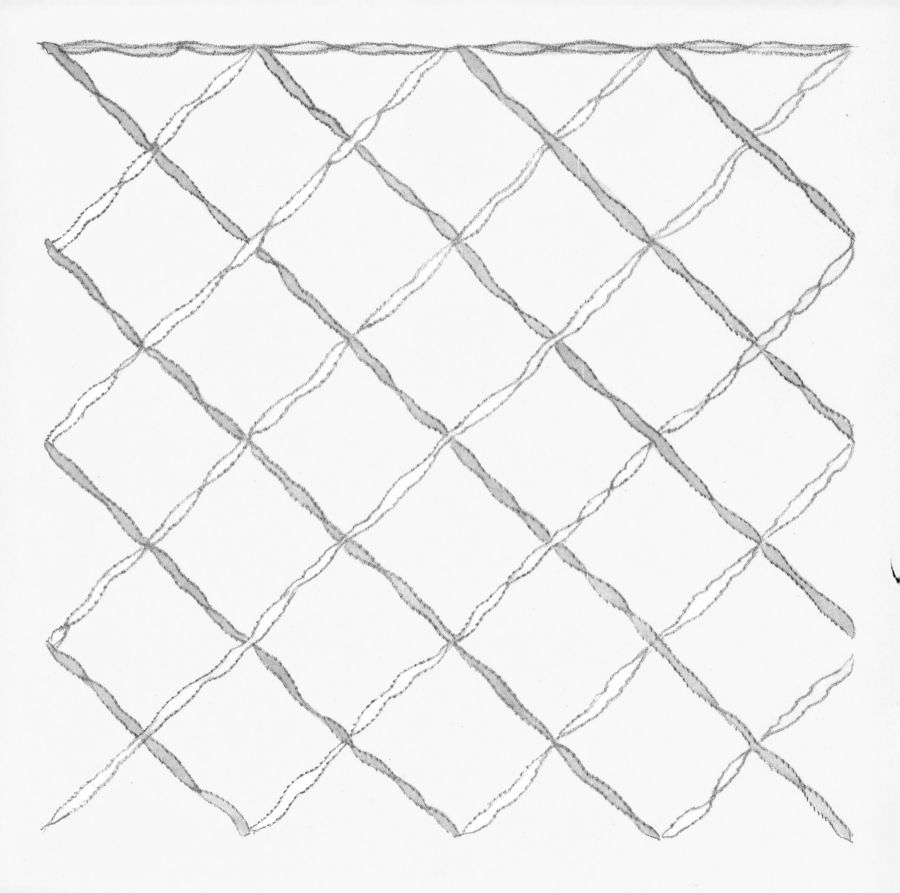